# GRANT MORRISON'S
# 18 DAYS ™

## VOLUME FOUR:
## THE RISING SON

# GRANT MORRISON'S 18 DAYS™

## Created by Grant Morrison

**CHAPTER 1 - THE SWORD OF ABHIMANYU**

| | |
|---|---|
| Script | Sarwat Chadda |
| Art | Francesco Biagini |
| Color | Sesha Sainan Devarajan |

**CHAPTER 2 - THE SON OF FATE**

| | |
|---|---|
| Script | Sarwat Chadda |
| Art | Francesco Biagini |
| Color | Sesha Sainan Devarajan |

**CHAPTER 3 - FORGOTTEN SONS PART 1**

| | |
|---|---|
| Script | Sarwat Chadda |
| Art | Ronilson Freire |
| Color | S. Sundarakannan |

**CHAPTER 4 - FORGOTTEN SONS PART 2**

| | |
|---|---|
| Script | Sarwat Chadda |
| Art | Ronilson Freire |
| Color | S. Sundarakannan |

**CHAPTER 5 - ART OF WAR**

| | |
|---|---|
| Script | Sarwat Chadda |
| Art | Francesco Biagini |
| Color | S. Sundarakannan |

## CHAPTER 6 - **THE CRUEL BLADE**

Script       Sarwat Chadda

Art          Francesco Biagini

Color        S. Sundarakannan

Cover                          SVP Creative
Mukesh Singh                   Jeevan J. Kang

Letters                        Publisher & CEO
Aditya Bidikar                 Sharad Devarajan

Print Production               Special Thanks
Nilesh S. Mahadik              Kristan Morrison
Rakesh B. Mahadik              Steven Lehrhoff
                               Ashish Avin

Editors
Sharad Devarajan
Ashwin Pande

Graphic India Founders
Sharad Devarajan
Gotham Chopra
Suresh Seetharaman

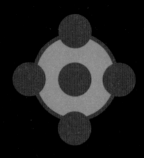

# CHAPTER 1
# Sword Of Abhimanyu

THERE. SIX YOJANS FROM HERE.

WHO LIVED HERE? WHAT LIVES DID THEY LEAD?

WHAT CALAMITY TURNED THIS CITY INTO A GRAVEYARD?

THE ANSWERS ARE LOST IN THE DUST.

# CHAPTER 2
# The Son of Fate

# CHAPTER 3
# Forgotten Sons Part 1

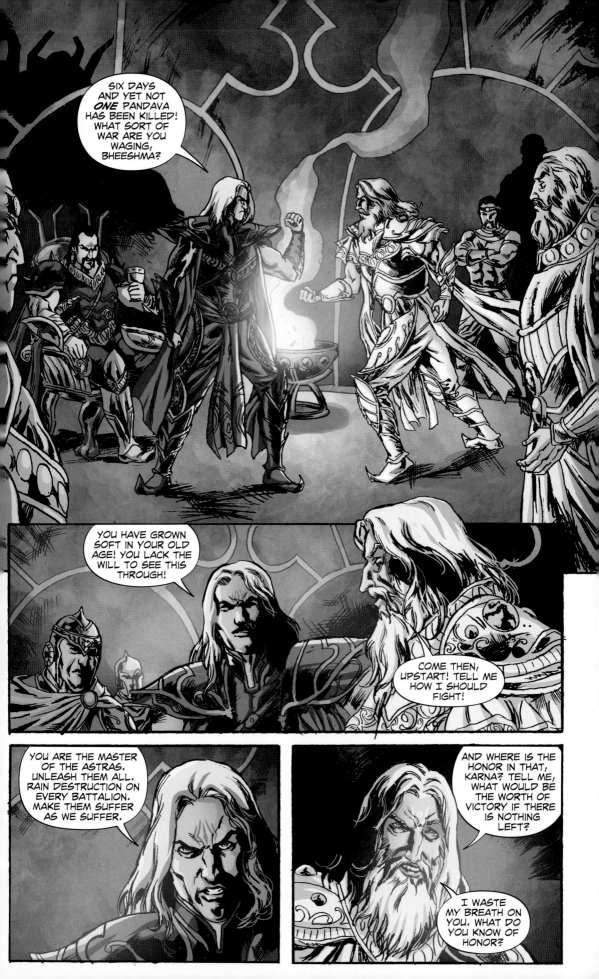

I'M LEAVING!

ABHIMANYU!

LET HIM GO AND COOL DOWN, ARJUNA. HE'S JUST IMPATIENT. LIKE ALL YOUNG MEN.

SO I SHOULD JUST GIVE INTO HIS DESIRES, BHIMA? HE THINKS THIS IS SOME SPORT! A GAME TO BE PLAYED!

PERHAPS HE IS READY, ARJUNA. PERHAPS YOU PROTECT HIM *TOO* MUCH. YOUR SON'S SKILLS ALMOST MATCH YOUR OWN. WHO COULD POSSIBLY STAND AGAINST HIM?

THE BOY'S RECKLESS, YUDISH. AND SO YOUNG.

LOOK AT US. WE HAVE SCARS. OLD WOUNDS THAT NEVER TRULY HEALED. ACHES THAT COME IN THE MORNING AND NO LONGER FADE AS THE SUN SETS. WE KNOW WHAT THE YOUNG DO NOT.

THAT WE ARE MORTAL AND OUR TIME IS BRIEF.

I WANT ABHIMANYU TO STAND IN THE SUN A WHILE LONGER, BROTHER.

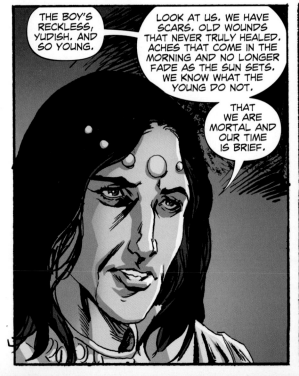

JUST LOOK AROUND A BIT, RIGHT? NO FIGHTING, UNDER-STOOD?

THE FIRST ARROW THAT FLIES IN OUR DIRECTION WE'RE COMING STRAIGHT BACK, OKAY?

OF COURSE! ABSOLUTELY!

FIRE HER UP!

I *KNOW* I'M GOING TO REGRET THIS...

WOO-HOO!

FRRRRRR

THE BOY... LOOKS LIKE *ME*. HOW IS THAT POSSIBLE?

HOW DO YOU THINK? ALL IT TAKES IS A WILLING WOMAN AND A FOOL.

SO WHAT SHOULD WE DO WITH THIS UNEXPECTED GUEST?

GIVE HIM A COIN AND CAST HIM BACK OUT ON THE STREET, WHERE HE BELONGS.

HE IS NO CONCERN OF MINE.

I THINK NOT. PERHAPS IT IS LONG PAST THE TIME YOU STARTED TAKING RESPONSIBILITY FOR YOUR ACTIONS. AND MISTAKES.

PERHAPS THAT MIGHT ENCOURAGE YOU TO MAKE LESS OF THEM.

YOU CANNOT BE SERIOUS! YOU WANT ME TO ACKNOWLEDGE HIM? THIS...*THING?*

THE BOY IS *YOURS*. DEAL WITH HIM.

WHAT DO YOU THINK OF DURMA?

HE BRINGS SHAME ON US ALL. I AM TUTOR TO *PRINCES*.

I WILL NOT TEACH HIM.

A CHILD SHOULD NOT BE ASHAMED OF HIS EXISTENCE. THAT IS THE FATHER'S FAULT.

MY ANSWER REMAINS THE SAME. HE CANNOT TRAIN WITH ROYALTY.

ASHWATHAMA SEEMS HAPPY IN HIS COMPANY.

MY SON? ANOTHER ONE OF MY FAILURES. A WARRIOR WITHOUT HONOR.

THEIR SILENCE INTRIGUES ME. I MEAN TO MAKE USE OF IT. WE ARE NOT ALL BORN TO BE WARRIORS, BELLOWING CHALLENGES ACROSS THE BATTLEFIELD.

SOME BATTLES ARE BEST FOUGHT IN SILENCE.

*ASSASSINS?* IS THAT WHAT YOU WISH? I WILL NOT HEAR OF IT!

# CHAPTER 4
# Forgotten Sons Part 2

HOW, ARJUNA? THE FOREST IS VAST. YOU COULD WASTE MONTHS SEARCHING AND FIND NOTHING.

GET OUT OF MY WAY, BROTHER.

WE NEED YOU HERE, ARJUNA. DURYODHANA'S DEMON BATTALIONS ARE ALMOST OVERWHELMING OUR FORCES. THE MEN NEED YOU.

I...

TRUST YOUR SON. YOU HAVE TRAINED HIM WELL. TRUST HIM TO SURVIVE THIS.

BUT YOUR PLACE IS HERE, AT THE HEAD OF MY ARMY.

TAKE YOUR POSITION, BROTHER.

VERY WELL, YUDISH.

I SHALL DO AS YOU COMMAND.

ONE OF THEM IS INJURED.

THE TRACKS LEAD NORTH. BACK TOWARDS THE PANDAVA LINES.

WE MUST HURRY...

AAARGH!

"...IF WE WANT TO KILL THEM."

WE'LL STOP FOR A MINUTE AND REST UP.

WE DON'T HAVE TIME. WE'RE MILES FROM--

I SAID WE'LL STOP.

LISTEN TO ME, PRINCE. THIS LEG'S SLOWING US DOWN.

I'M SLOWING US DOWN. YOU'LL MOVE FASTER WITHOUT ME.

SO YOU WANT ME TO ABANDON YOU HERE TO DIE?

FAIR ENOUGH.

I JUST DIDN'T THINK YOU'D BE THE SORT TO GIVE UP SO EASILY.

A BLIND MAN COULD FOLLOW THIS TRAIL.

THEY ARE RUSHING. THEY KNOW THEY'RE IN NO STATE TO FACE US.

IT WOULD NOT BE A... FAIR FIGHT.

A FAIR FIGHT? IS THERE SUCH A THING?

EACH WARRIOR SEEKS ADVANTAGE OVER HIS ENEMY, TO MAKE THE BATTLE UNFAIR. HOW ELSE DOES HE ENSURE VICTORY?

I AGREE. DURYODHANA HAS GIVEN US A TASK TO ACCOMPLISH. THAT IS ALL THAT MATTERS.

LET OLD MEN LIKE BHEESHMA AND DRONA DEBATE WHAT IS FAIR OR NOT...

THAK

GOOD.
VERY
GOOD.

WE SHALL
CONTINUE YOUR
LESSONS
TOMORROW.

BUT
FIRST...

...CLEAN
THIS MESS
UP.

FIRST THING I'M GOING TO DO IS HAVE A MEAL. A *FEAST*.

PILES OF RICE. A CAULDRON OF DAL. A FLOCK OF CHICKENS.

ALL WASHED DOWN WITH FIVE BARRELS OF WINE.

YOU SOUND JUST LIKE MY UNCLE BHIMA. HAVING HIS BREAKFAST.

YOU THINK THEY'RE LOOKING FOR US? FOR YOU?

DOES IT MATTER?

WE ARE NOT FAR. ANOTHER TEN MILES TO OUR LINES.

THEN WE'LL HAVE TO DEAL WITH MY FATHER'S FURY.

THERE'S SOMEONE ELSE

THINK I CAN'T HEAR YOU? THAT I CAN'T SMELL YOU? OR SEE YOU?

YOU ONLY SERVE DARKNESS...

I *AM* DARKNESS!

WE SHOULD HUNT THEM DOWN, AS THEY DID US. FINISH THEM OFF ONCE AND FOR ALL.

LET THEM FLEE.

BUT--

LET THEM FLEE.

YOU HAVE SEEN MY TRUE SELF. I DID NOT WISH THIS. I AM SORRY I HAVE SHAMED YOU.

THERE IS NO SHAME FIGHTING BESIDE THE SON OF BHIMA. THAT IS WHO YOU ARE, ISN'T IT?

...YES.

IT IS TIME YOU TOOK YOUR RIGHTFUL PLACE, GATOK, BESIDE US, BESIDE YOUR FATHER.

NO. A PROMISE WAS MADE, THAT I WOULD NOT FIGHT IN THIS WAR. I CANNOT LET MY FATHER KNOW I'VE BROKEN IT.

IF OUR FRIENDSHIP MEANS ANYTHING, SWEAR TO ME YOU'LL KEEP MY SECRET, ABHIMANYU.

FRIENDSHIP? WE ARE NOT FRIENDS, GATOK, WE ARE BROTHERS.

I WILL KEEP YOUR SECRET. I SWEAR IT.

I CAN SEE OUR CAMP FIRES, THEY ARE NOT FAR.

LET'S GO HOME.

# CHAPTER 5
# The Art of War

# CHAPTER 6
# The Cruel Blade